100 YEARS OF POPULAR

Series Editor:
Carol Cuellar

Editorial and Production:
Artemis Music Limited

Design and Production:
JPCreativeGroup.com

Published 2003

International Music Publications Limited
Griffin House 161 Hammersmith Road London W6 8BS England

CONTENTS

TITLE	PAGE
AIN'T SHE SWEET	12
AM I BLUE?	16
AMONG MY SOUVENIRS	20
BABY FACE	24
BASIN STREET BLUES	28
BECAUSE MY BABY DON'T MEAN MAYBE NOW	32
BUGLE CALL RAG	9
CAROLINA MOON	36
CHICAGO (THAT TODDLING TOWN)	40
A CUP OF COFFEE, A SANDWICH AND YOU	44
DANCE LITTLE LADY	52
DEEP IN MY HEART, DEAR	60
DELANEY'S DONKEY	68
THE DESERT SONG	72
DINAH	76
DOES THE SPEARMINT LOSE ITS FLAVOUR (ON THE BEDPOST OVERNIGHT) ?	49
DON'T BRING LULU	80
DOWN YONDER	82
DRINKING SONG	86
FASCINATNG RHYTHM	90
FIVE FOOT TWO, EYES OF BLUE (HAS ANYBODY SEEN MY GIRL?)	95
GIRL OF MY DREAMS	98
HALFWAY DOWN THE STAIRS	106
HAPPY DAYS AND LONELY NIGHTS	108
HOW LONG HAS THIS BEEN GOING ON?	101
I BELONG TO GLASGOW	112
I CAN'T GIVE YOU ANYTHING BUT LOVE	114
I WISH I COULD SHIMMY LIKE MY SISTER KATE	118
I WONDER WHERE MY BABY IS TONIGHT	124
I'LL BE WITH YOU IN APPLE BLOSSOM TIME	130
I'M JUST WILD ABOUT HARRY	132
I'M NOBODY'S BABY	144
I'VE NEVER SEEN A STRAIGHT BANANA	136
IF YOU KNEW SUSIE	140
INDIAN LOVE CALL	146
IT HAD TO BE YOU	121
JUST A GIGOLO	152
K-RA-ZY FOR YOU	156
THE LAZIEST GAL IN TOWN	160
LET'S DO IT (LET'S FALL IN LOVE)	168

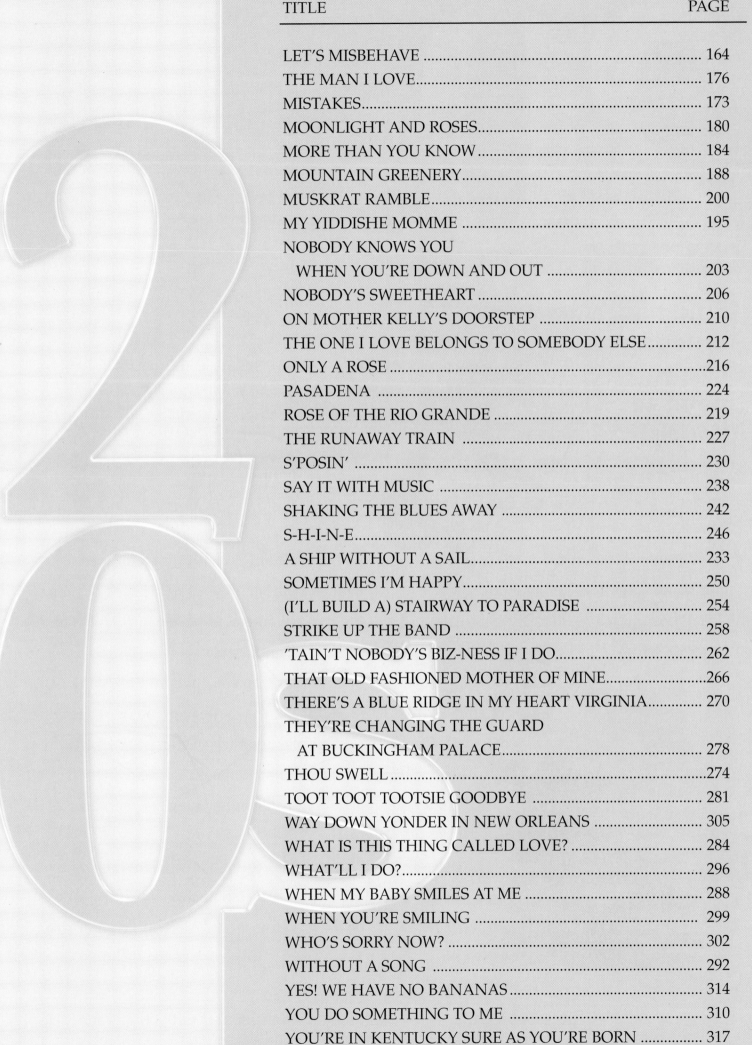

TITLE	PAGE
LET'S MISBEHAVE	164
THE MAN I LOVE	176
MISTAKES	173
MOONLIGHT AND ROSES	180
MORE THAN YOU KNOW	184
MOUNTAIN GREENERY	188
MUSKRAT RAMBLE	200
MY YIDDISHE MOMME	195
NOBODY KNOWS YOU WHEN YOU'RE DOWN AND OUT	203
NOBODY'S SWEETHEART	206
ON MOTHER KELLY'S DOORSTEP	210
THE ONE I LOVE BELONGS TO SOMEBODY ELSE	212
ONLY A ROSE	216
PASADENA	224
ROSE OF THE RIO GRANDE	219
THE RUNAWAY TRAIN	227
S'POSIN'	230
SAY IT WITH MUSIC	238
SHAKING THE BLUES AWAY	242
S-H-I-N-E	246
A SHIP WITHOUT A SAIL	233
SOMETIMES I'M HAPPY	250
(I'LL BUILD A) STAIRWAY TO PARADISE	254
STRIKE UP THE BAND	258
'TAIN'T NOBODY'S BIZ-NESS IF I DO	262
THAT OLD FASHIONED MOTHER OF MINE	266
THERE'S A BLUE RIDGE IN MY HEART VIRGINIA	270
THEY'RE CHANGING THE GUARD AT BUCKINGHAM PALACE	278
THOU SWELL	274
TOOT TOOT TOOTSIE GOODBYE	281
WAY DOWN YONDER IN NEW ORLEANS	305
WHAT IS THIS THING CALLED LOVE?	284
WHAT'LL I DO?	296
WHEN MY BABY SMILES AT ME	288
WHEN YOU'RE SMILING	299
WHO'S SORRY NOW?	302
WITHOUT A SONG	292
YES! WE HAVE NO BANANAS	314
YOU DO SOMETHING TO ME	310
YOU'RE IN KENTUCKY SURE AS YOU'RE BORN	317

20s

Bold and brooding... lively and pensive... hopeful and uncertain...

the 1920s were an intricately woven tapestry of diverse and sometimes conflicting moods.

Unsettled, uncertain, and often confusing, but never dull, they were exhilarating years that gave those who experienced them a keen sense of history. One could not live through the '20s without being aware of the pivotal role that the decade was destined to play in shaping the world's future.

The Great War (1914-1918) had forever changed the secure and stable sensibilities of the Edwardian era. Although the conflict had been won, and the Kaiser vanquished, a sense of apprehension still lingered during the '20s. Memories of the carnage in the trenches were still fresh. A new "Lost Generation" of writers and artists had come out of the war years angered, disillusioned, and fragmented.

Closer to home, the aftermath of the war and the swift advance of technology had challenged traditional class and gender roles. The General Strike of 1926 highlighted the discontent felt in many quarters of society. Women were stepping out of the shadows to assume a more prominent role in commercial, cultural, and political life. (In 1928, women were granted the same voting rights as men in the UK.) Meanwhile, young people from even the most respectable homes were demonstrating a rebellious streak that was quite unlike anything seen in earlier generations.

Yet, despite their uncertainty and apprehension, the people of the '20s looked forward to the future with a high degree of optimism. The first British Empire Exhibition, which opened at Wembley in 1924, showcased the recovery that the nation and her colonies had made from the Great War.

Looking about the bustling city of London in the '20s, one could readily justify a strong sense of optimism. Technology had brought a new level of convenience to the lives of most Europeans and Americans. Charles Lindbergh shrunk the distance between Europe and the US with his trans-Atlantic flight in May 1927. The development of electronic appliances freed women from many time-consuming household chores. On November 14, 1922, the BBC began airing daily radio broadcasts, giving the nation its first mass media outlet, and making Big Ben time signals part of daily life.

A Rich Musical Mix

The music of the '20s reflected both the apprehensions and expectations of the era. Contrasted to the decades that came before it, the '20s served up history's most varied smorgasbord of popular music, a feast that included everything from the sentimentally nostalgic "I'll Be With You In Apple Blossom Time", to the unapologetically sensual "Nobody Knows You When You're Down And Out" by the legendary American blues artist Bessie Smith.

Popular music also offered the people of the '20s an opportunity to escape from the disquieting changes that were swirling around them. The decade that brought the raw blues style of Bessie Smith to the forefront of the national psyche also was a golden era of novelty songs. Upbeat, witty, and often whimsical, these tunes were warmly embraced by fans in the UK and the rest of Europe, as well as in America.

Among the most popular novelty tunes was the Frank Silver and Irving Cohn composition "Yes! We Have No Bananas", which was featured in the Eddie Cantor stage production *Make It Snappy*. The song, with a simple chorus, "Yes we have no bananas, we have no bananas today", that was destined to become world-famous, was supposedly inspired by a conversation the writers had with a street fruit vendor in the US. Whether or not this actually transpired, we cannot say, but one thing is certain, the Silver-Cohn song became a cultural phenomenon that was still very familiar to Europeans and Americans at the end of the 20th century.

Another lighthearted song of the '20s that would resonate with fans for decades to come was "Ain't She Sweet". Written by the successful team of Jack Yellen and Milton Ager, the song was a hit on both sides of the Atlantic for Ben Bernie in the '20s. Over three decades later, "Ain't She Sweet" was recorded by a rising young British group called The Beatles. The Yellen and Ager tune

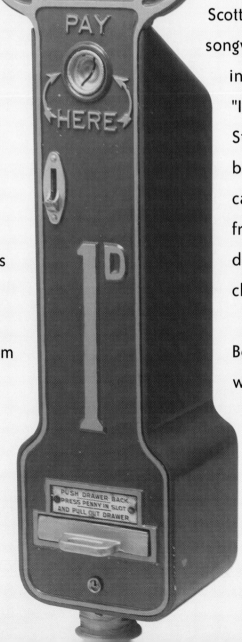

became a staple of The Beatles' live performances in the late '50s and early '60s. The Fab Four even had a hit with their recording of the song, which recounts a young man's unbridled infatuation with a pretty girl.

Songs For All People

Talented artists of the '20s often used a wry sense of humour in their songs to address serious social issues and give voice to the concerns of everyday people. Scottish actor, musician, and songwriter Will Fyffe achieved international fame with his hit "I Belong To Glasgow". Striking a delicate balance between wit and anger, Fyffe captures the pride and frustrations of a self-described "common working chap" in his song.

Born in 1885 in Dundee, Fyffe would be identified with the common folk throughout his career, but few things about the man himself were ordinary. As a youth, he toured Scotland with his father's stock company. By the time he was fifteen, he was already playing Hamlet. During the '20s, he was widely acclaimed as a musician and entertainer, receiving top billing when he appeared at the London Pavilion in 1921.

The '20s were also a time of musical innovations. Jazz, which grew out of the African-American community in New Orleans during the century's early years, achieved an international following during this decade. In Europe, venues such as London's Savoy Hotel became centres of jazz for a new generation of fans.

A New Voice For Women

Another breakthrough took place in the area of women's music. Although female artists had always been a vital part of the music scene, it wasn't until the '20s, the decade of the free-spirited "flapper", that women were able to shed the demure image of an earlier age and express their own sensual desires in song without apology.

American Sophie Tucker personified the new brash female artist of the '20s. The irrepressible Tucker began singing as a child in her parents' restaurant, in part to escape the drudgery of serving diners and washing dishes. Although plump and rather plain, she was determined to establish herself as an

entertainer. She landed a part in the Zeigfield Follies and attracted a loyal following of fans as a result of her powerful stage presence, heartfelt honesty, and risqué banter.

In 1922, Tucker made the first of what would become many tours of the UK. She starred in *Round In Fifty*, Sax Rohmer's popular revue based on the Jules Verne classic Around the World In 80 Days. (Born in Birmingham, Rohmer created the famous character Fu Manchu.)

Following the success of *Round In Fifty*, Tucker would return to the UK many times throughout

WARDONIA For BETTER SHAVES

WARDONIA BARREL HOLE BLADE

SOLE MAKERS
THOMAS WARD & SONS LTD WARDONIA WORKS SHEFFIELD I

her long career, becoming a popular entertainer at London's Kit Kat Club. Upon her return from a 1925 tour of Europe, Tucker created quite a controversy in the US, when she stepped off her ship wearing trousers!

Defying convention in a male-dominated world was indeed a Sophie Tucker trademark. Big and brassy, Tucker took no small measure of delight in challenging her audience. Yet there was more than one side to this gifted performer. Tucker's powerful voice exuded a warmth and sensitivity that made her well suited to sing sentimental tunes such as "The Man I Love".

How fitting it was, then, that this woman who broke down barriers and mixed brash confidence with tender vulnerability should reach the zenith of her career during the '20s, a decade that exhibited many of the same wonderful contradictions. So, go ahead and enjoy this collection of songs made famous by Tucker and the other great artists, male and female, of the '20s, an exciting time of new ideas and great music.

Ten Things That First Appeared In The '20s

1. The first wireless phone call (New York to London via radio in 1923).

2. Talking motion picture (*The Jazz Singer* from Warner Bros. starring Al Jolson, 1927).

3. Women's track and field competition in the Summer Olympics (Amsterdam).

4. MG Special sports cars.

5. King George V Dock (London, 1921).

6. Prepared baby foods.

7. Inflatable beach ball.

8. Penicillin (Alexander Fleming, St. Mary's Hospital, London).

9. Insulin treatment for diabetes.

10. Agatha Christie detective novel.

BUGLE CALL RAG

Words and Music by JOHN PETTIS, BILLY MEYERS
and ELMER SCHOEBEL

AIN'T SHE SWEET

Words by JACK YELLEN
Music by MILTON AGER

Lyrics:

There she is!___
Tell me where,

There she is!___ There's what keeps me up at night.___
tell me where___ have you seen one just like that?___

AM I BLUE?

Words by GRANT CLARKE
Music by HARRY AKST

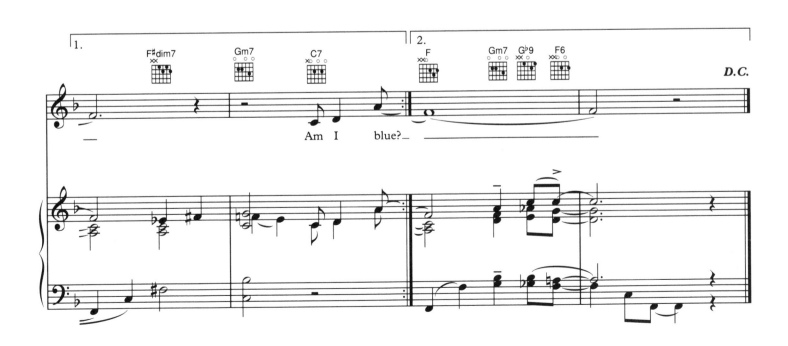

AMONG MY SOUVENIRS

Words by EDGAR LESLIE
Music by HORATIO NICHOLLS

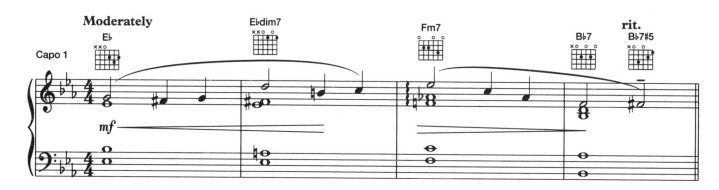

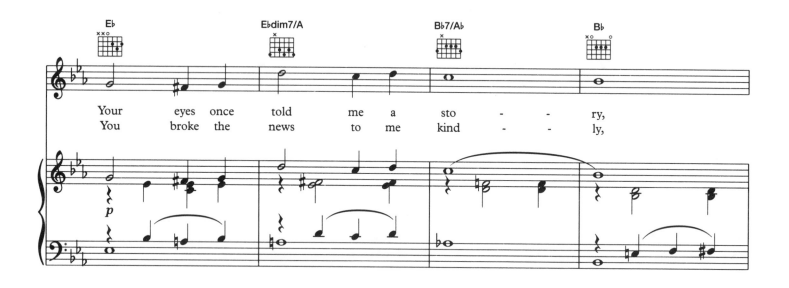

Your eyes once told me a sto - - ry,
You broke the news to me kind - - ly,

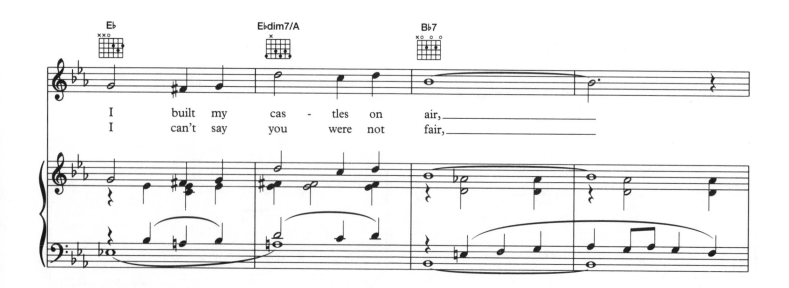

I built my cas - tles on air,____
I can't say you were not fair,____

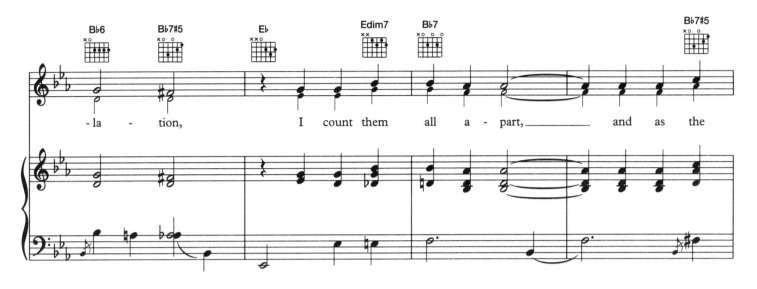

-la - tion, I count them all a - part,_____ and as the

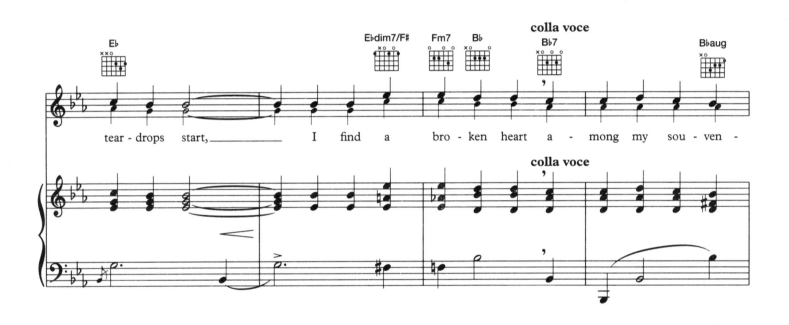

colla voce

tear - drops start,_____ I find a bro - ken heart a - mong my sou - ven -

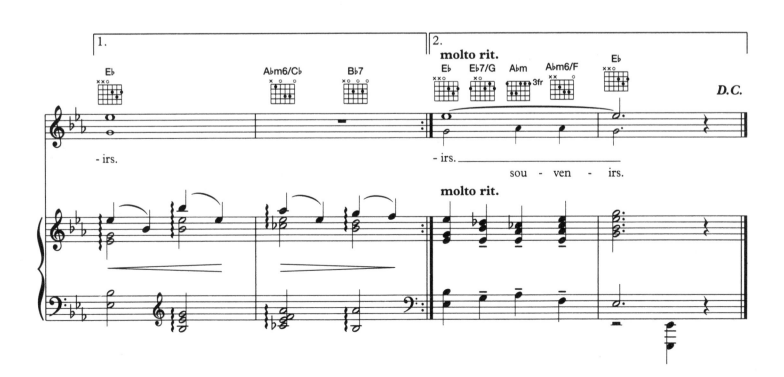

1.

- irs.

2. molto rit.

- irs._____ sou - ven - irs.

D.C.

BABY FACE

Words and Music by BENNY DAVIS and HARRY AKST

BASIN STREET BLUES

Words and Music by SPENCER WILLIAMS

BECAUSE MY BABY DON'T MEAN MAYBE NOW

Words and Music by WALTER DONALDSON

Ev - 'ry - thing seems love - ly, the world is so se - rene, when
Ev - 'ry - thing is ro - sy, I feel so, so and so, when

I say things are love - ly, you know just what I mean. It
I say things are ro - sy, I know you know I know.

so I say: 'Life is short and migh-ty sweet, but

I know mine is quite com-plete,— be-cause my ba-by don't mean 'may-be'

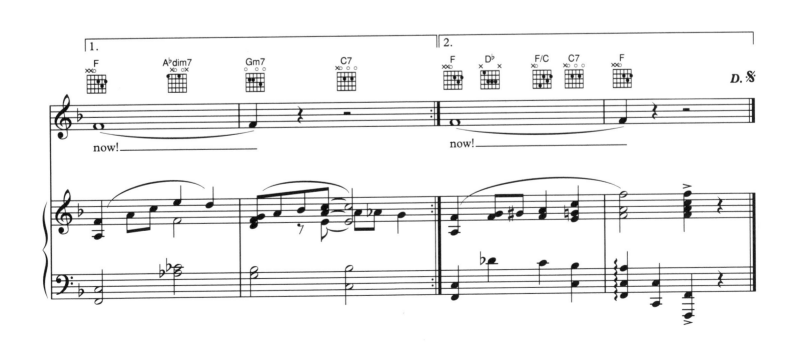

now! _____   now! _____   D. %

CAROLINA MOON

Words and Music by BENNY DAVIS and JOE BURKE

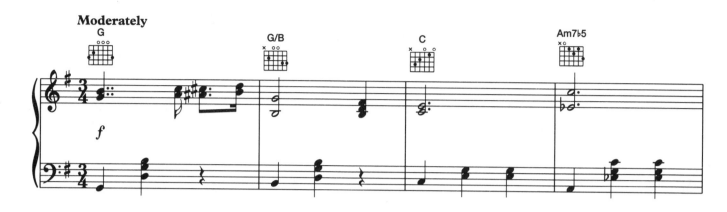

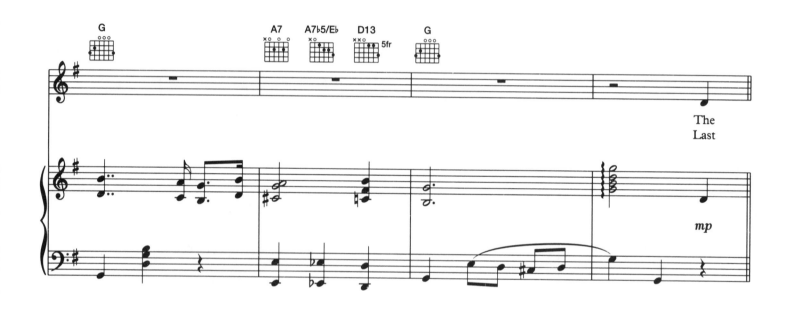

The
Last

moon   was shin - ing bright   in Ca - ro - li - - na   the
night   I had a dream   of Ca - ro - li - - na.   I

CHICAGO (THAT TODDLING TOWN)

Words and Music by FRED FISHER

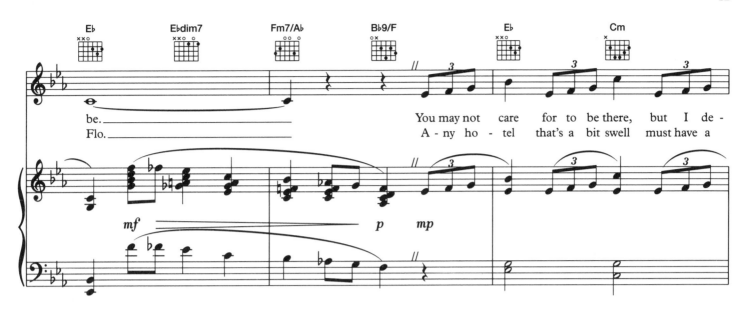

You may not care for to be there, but I de-
A - ny ho - tel that's a bit swell must have a

- clare, you're not a - ware just where to go.
band right here on hand or else they're cheap.

When you're in
If you'll in -

town, just call a-round, right there I'm found, real - ly you ought to know.
- vest, you'll find a guest, they'll ne - ver rest, they're danc-ing while they sleep.

Chi -

A CUP OF COFFEE, A SANDWICH AND YOU

Words by AL DUBIN and BILLY ROSE
Music by JOSEPH MEYER

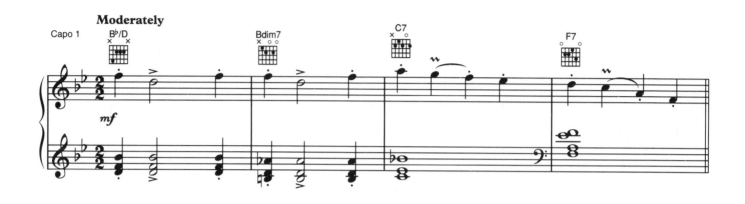

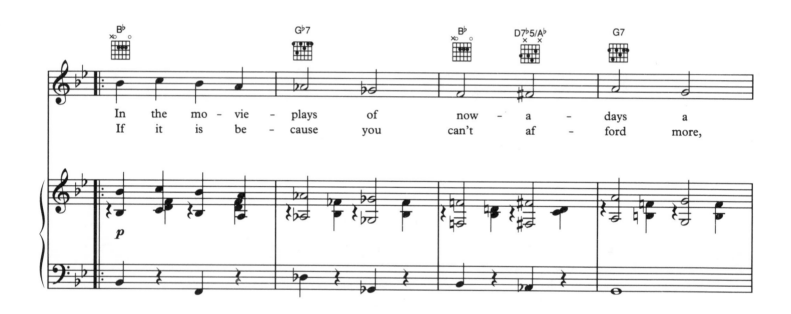

In the mo - vie - plays of now - a - days a
If it is be - cause you can't af - ford more,

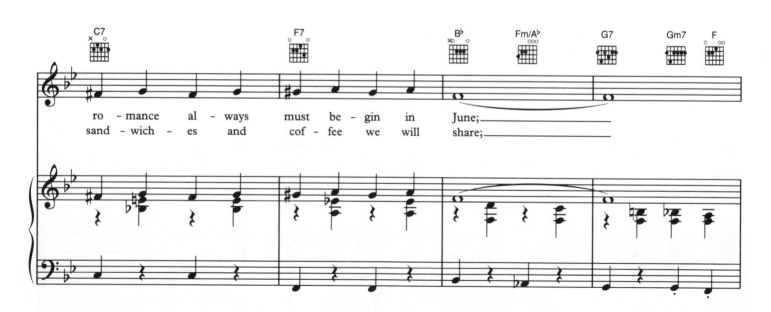

ro - mance al - ways must be - gin in June;
sand - wich - es and cof - fee we will share;

DOES THE SPEARMINT LOSE ITS FLAVOUR (ON THE BEDPOST OVERNIGHT)?

Words by BILLY ROSE and MARTY BLOOM
Music by ERNEST BREUER

DANCE LITTLE LADY

Words and Music by NOEL COWARD

Though you're on-ly sev-en-teen, far too much of life you've seen,

syn-co-pa-ted child. May-be if you on-ly knew

wait, let the caul - dron bub - ble, jus - ti - fy your

fate. Dance, dance, dance lit - tle la - dy! Dance, dance, dance lit - tle la - dy!

Leave to - mor - row be - hind.

tempo di Charleston

When the sax - o - phone gives a wic - ked moan, Charle - ston,_ hey! Hey!_

tempo di Charleston

DEEP IN MY HEART, DEAR

Words by DOROTHY DONNELLY
Music by SIGMUND ROMBERG

(She) Of love I of-ten heard,___ and all its joy,___ how ev-ery

heart is stirred,___ both girl and boy,___ but though in love a-lone___ is ten-der

Warner/Chappell Music Ltd, London W1Y 3FA and Redwood Music Ltd, London NW1 8BD

eyes look in mine, with - in them a soft flame gent - ly glows._____ (Both) The

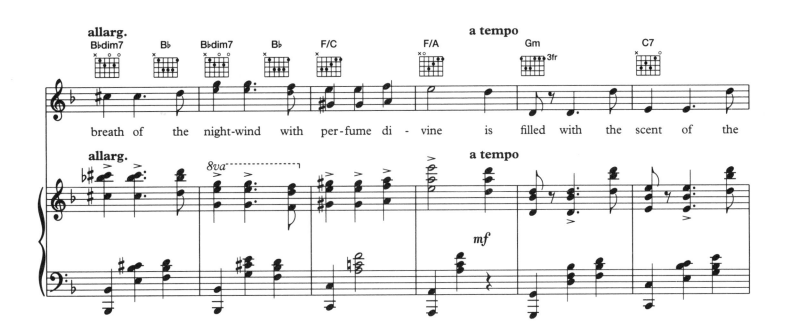

breath of the night-wind with per-fume di - vine is filled with the scent of the

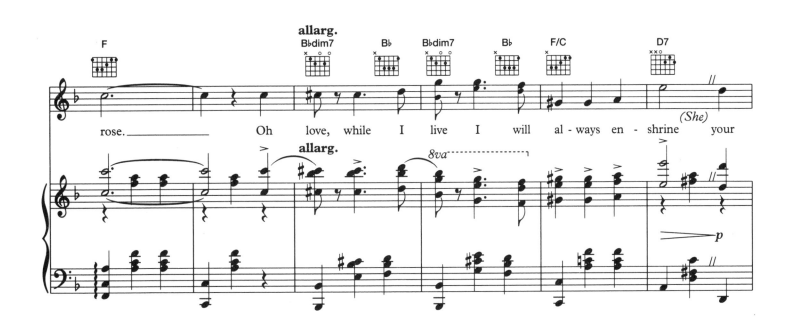

rose._____ Oh love, while I live I will al - ways en - shrine your

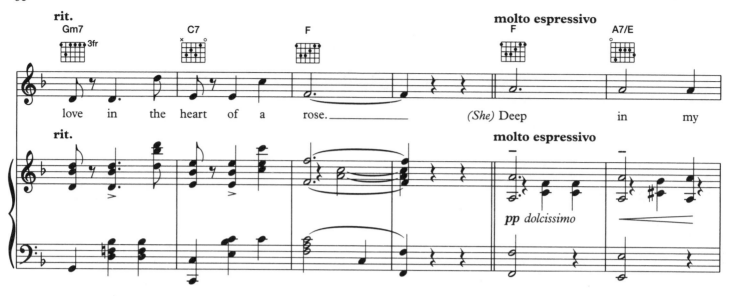
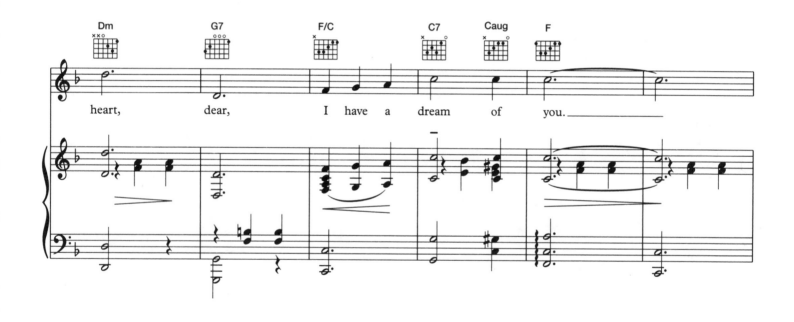
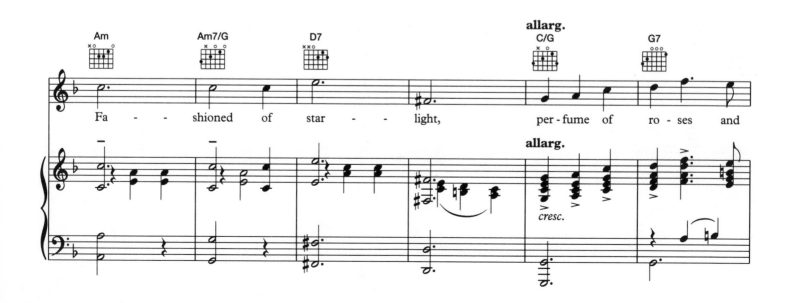

DELANEY'S DONKEY

Words and Music by WILLIAM HARGREAVES

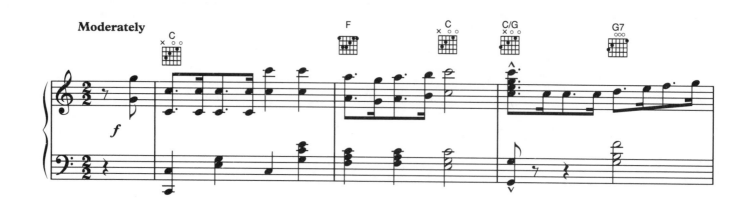

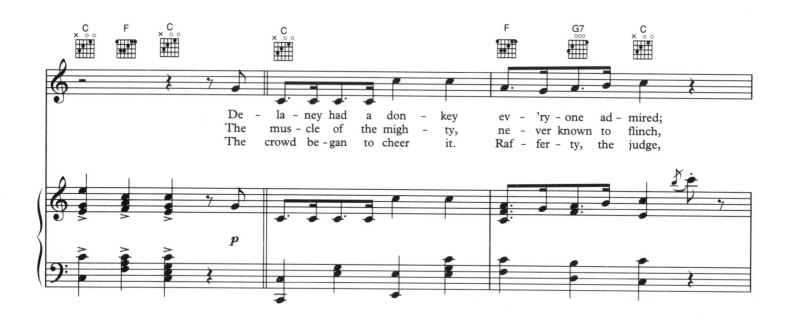

De - la - ney had a don - key ev - 'ry - one ad - mired;
The mus - cle of the migh - ty, ne - ver known to flinch,
The crowd be - gan to cheer it. Raf - fer - ty, the judge,

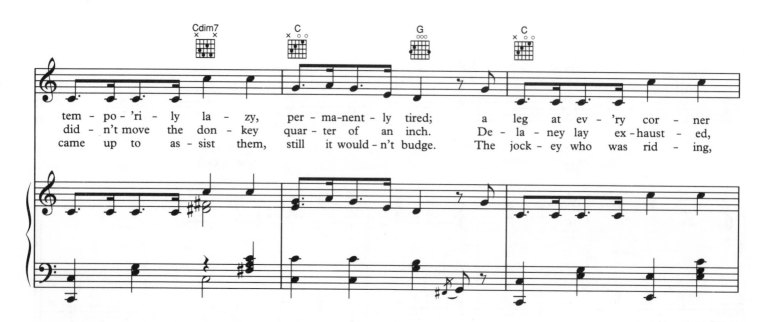

tem - po - 'ri - ly la - zy, per - ma - nent - ly tired; a leg at ev - 'ry cor - ner
did - n't move the don - key quar - ter of an inch. De - la - ney lay ex - haust - ed,
came up to as - sist them, still it would - n't budge. The jock - ey who was rid - ing,

THE DESERT SONG

Words by OTTO HARBACH and OSCAR HAMMERSTEIN II
Music by SIGMUND ROMBERG

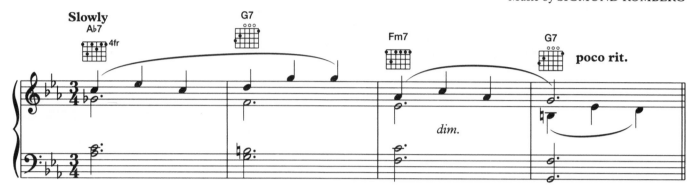

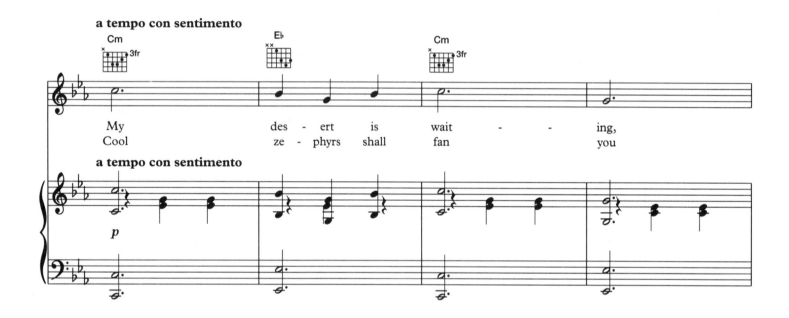

My des - ert is wait - - ing,
Cool ze - phyrs shall fan you

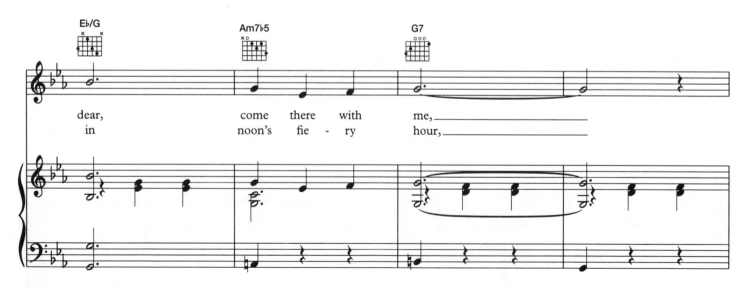

dear, come there with me,_____
in noon's fie - ry hour,_____

DINAH

Words by SAM LEWIS and JOE YOUNG
Music by HARRY AKST

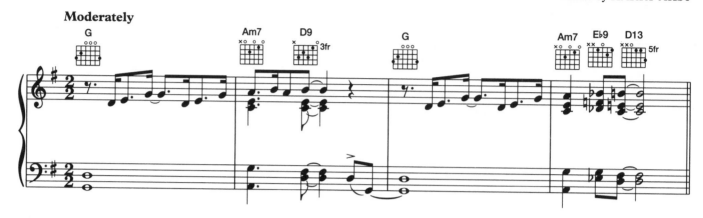

Ca - ro - li - na_____ gave me Di - nah,_____
I a - dore her,_____ cra - zy for her,_____

I'm the proud - est one be - neath the Dix - ie sun.
put me on a choo - choo that takes me to her.

DON'T BRING LULU

Words by BILLY ROSE and LEW BROWN
Music by RAY HENDERSON

Now you can bring Pearl, she's a darn nice girl, but don't bring Lu - lu.

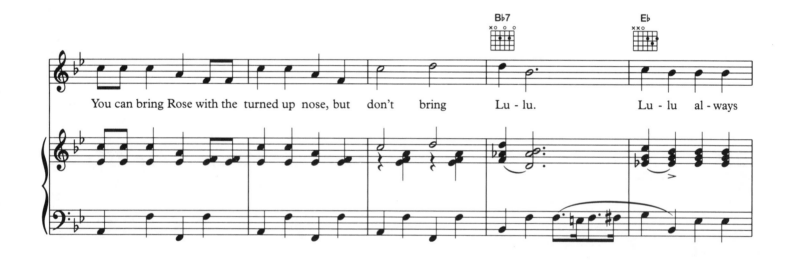

You can bring Rose with the turned up nose, but don't bring Lu - lu. Lu - lu al - ways

wants to do what we boys don't want her to, Ev - ery time she starts a - round,

Francis Day & Hunter Ltd, London WC2H 0EA and Redwood Music Ltd, London NW1 8BD

DOWN YONDER

Words and Music by L WOLFE GILBERT

DRINKING SONG

Words by DOROTHY DONNELLY
Music by SIGMUND ROMBERG

FASCINATING RHYTHM

Music and Lyrics by
GEORGE GERSHWIN and IRA GERSHWIN

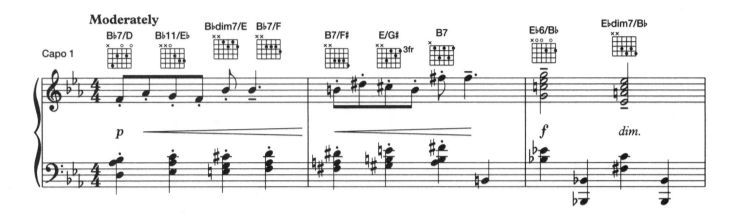

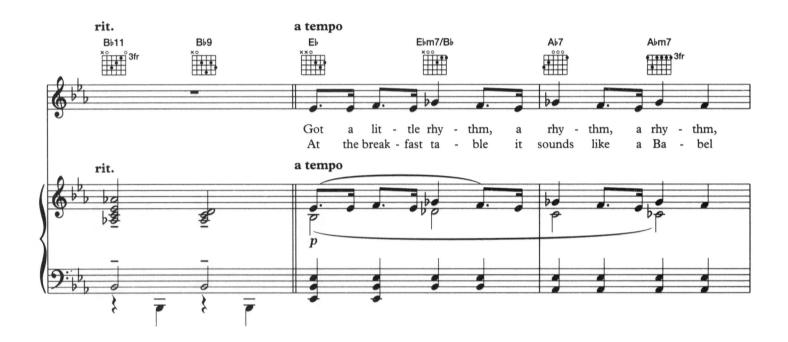

Got a lit - tle rhy - thm, a rhy - thm, a rhy - thm,
At the break - fast ta - ble it sounds like a Ba - bel

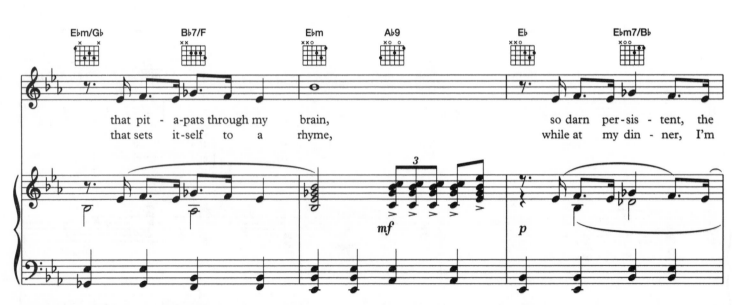

that pit - a-pats through my brain,
that sets it-self to a rhyme,
so darn per-sis - tent, the
while at my din - ner, I'm

day is - n't dis - tant, when it' - ll drive me in - sane.
sure get - ting thin - ner through mas - ti - cat - ing rag - time.

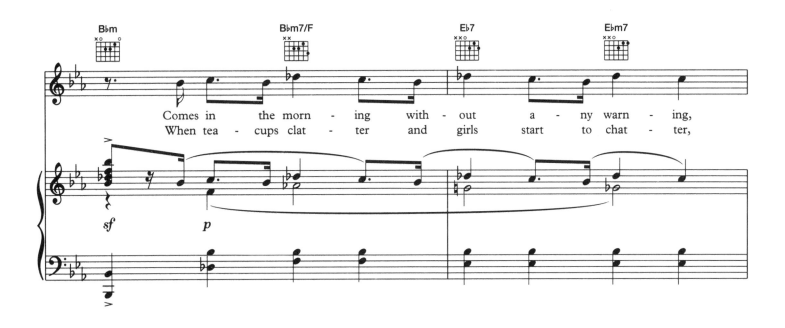

Comes in the morn - ing with - out a - ny warn - ing,
When tea - cups clat - ter and girls start to chat - ter,

and hangs a - round __ all day. I'll have to sneak up to it
the rhy - thm's there __ all right. The thing will ne - ver leave me,

FIVE FOOT TWO, EYES OF BLUE
(HAS ANYBODY SEEN MY GIRL?)

Words by JOE YOUNG and SAM LEWIS
Music by RAY HENDERSON

Five foot two, eyes of blue, but oh, what those five foot can do,— has

a-ny-bo-dy seen my girl?

GIRL OF MY DREAMS

Words and Music by SUNNY CLAPP

Dear, it seems years since we part - - ed, years full of
Though I've tried hard to for - get you, and though my

tears and re - gret,_____ I've been a - lone, bro - ken heart - -
love is in vain,_____ I live for the hours I'm with

HOW LONG HAS THIS BEEN GOING ON?

Music and Lyrics by GEORGE GERSHWIN and IRA GERSHWIN

HALFWAY DOWN THE STAIRS

Words by A. A. MILNE
Music by HOWARD FRASER-SIMSON

HAPPY DAYS AND LONELY NIGHTS

Words by BILLY ROSE
Music by FRED FISHER

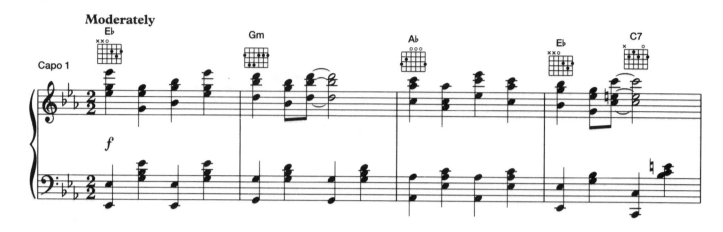

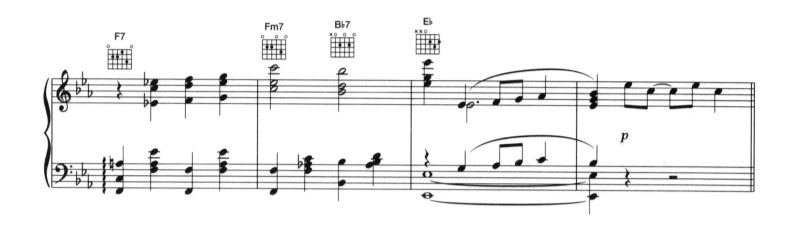

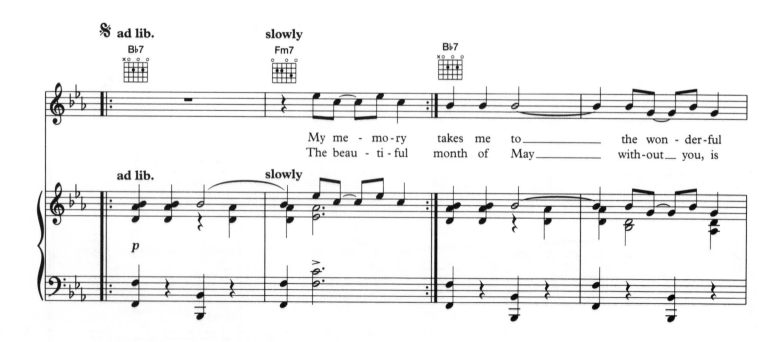

My me - mo - ry takes me to_____ the won - der - ful
The beau - ti - ful month of May_____ with - out_ you, is

I BELONG TO GLASGOW

Words and Music by WILL FYFFE

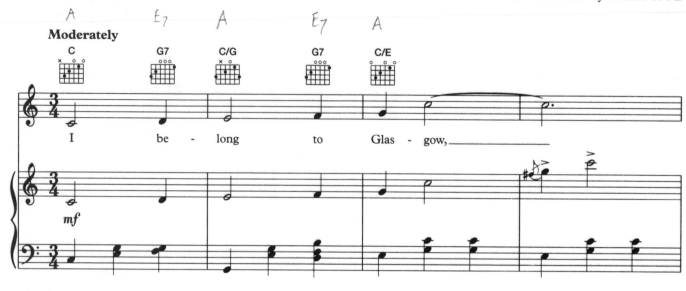

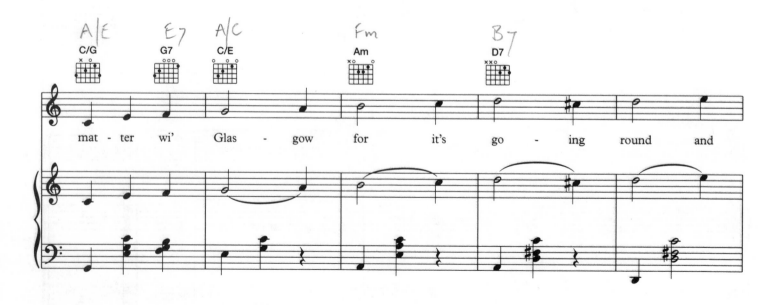

I CAN'T GIVE YOU ANYTHING BUT LOVE

Words by DOROTHY FIELDS
Music by JIMMY McHUGH

Gee, but it's tough to be broke, kid,_____ it's not a
Rome was-n't built in a day, kid,_____ you have to

joke, kid, it's a curse, think that you ought to be know - ing,_____ my luck is
pay, kid, for what you get, but I am will - ing to wait, dear,_____ your lit - tle

go - ing____ from bad to worse. Who knows, some-day I will
mate, dear,____ will not for - get. You have a life - time be -

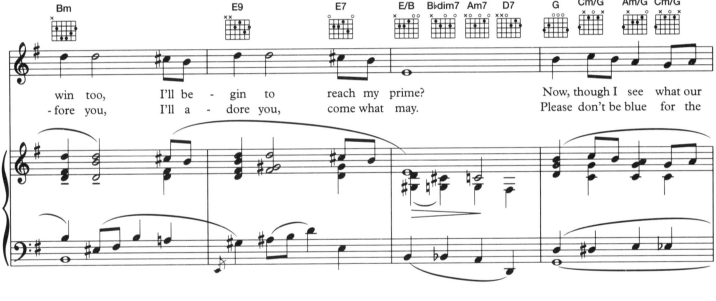

win too, I'll be - gin to reach my prime? Now, though I see what our
-fore you, I'll a - dore you, come what may. Please don't be blue for the

end is,____ all I can spend is just my time.
pre - sent,____ when it's so plea - sant to hear you say:

poco rall.

I WISH I COULD SHIMMY LIKE MY SISTER KATE

Words and Music by ARMAND J PIRON

IT HAD TO BE YOU

Words by GUS KAHN
Music by ISHAM JONES

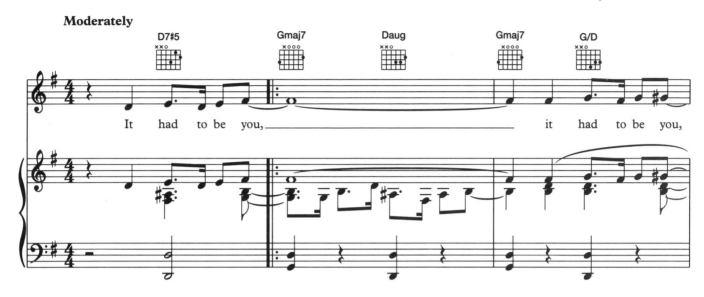

It had to be you,_____ it had to be you,

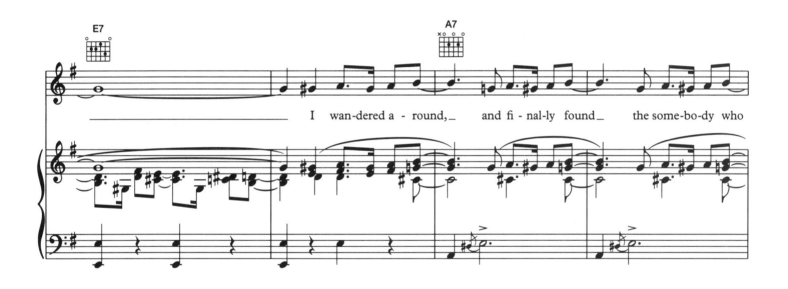

_____ I wan-dered a - round,_ and fi - nal-ly found_ the some-bo-dy who

_____ could make me be true,_____

I WONDER WHERE MY BABY IS TONIGHT

Words by GUS KAHN
Music by WALTER DONALDSON

I burned up ev-'ry let-ter, and thought that I'd feel bet-ter;
I know she said 'for-get me', and so I wish she'd let me;

I put a-way her pic-ture too.
why does she haunt me night and day?

I'LL BE WITH YOU IN APPLE BLOSSOM TIME

Words by NEVILLE FLEESON
Music by ALBERT VON TILZER

I'll be with you in ap - ple blos - som time,

I'll be with you to change your name to mine,

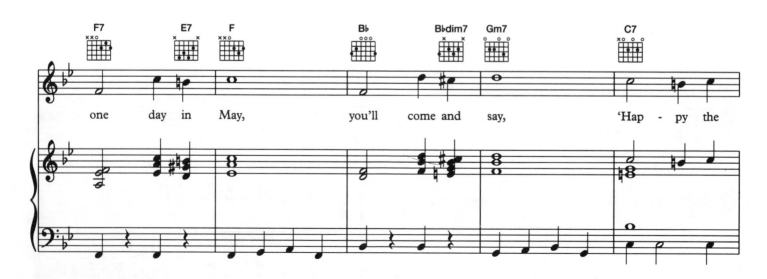

one day in May, you'll come and say, 'Hap - py the

I'M JUST WILD ABOUT HARRY

Words and Music by NOBLE SISSLE and EUBIE BLAKE

I'VE NEVER SEEN A STRAIGHT BANANA

Words and Music by TED WAITE

I've seen lots of fun-ny things in my time, but there's
I've seen cab-ba-ges, I have, with nobs on, I've seen

one thing that I've not seen up to now._____ For
love-ly red to-ma-toes turn-ing blue._____ I

IF YOU KNEW SUSIE

Words by BUDDY DE SYLVA
Music by JOSEPH MEYER

I have got a sweet-ie known as Su - sie,

Su - sie, in the words of Shake-speare she's a

Su-sie has a per-fect re-pu - ta - tion,

no one ev - er saw her on a

141

142

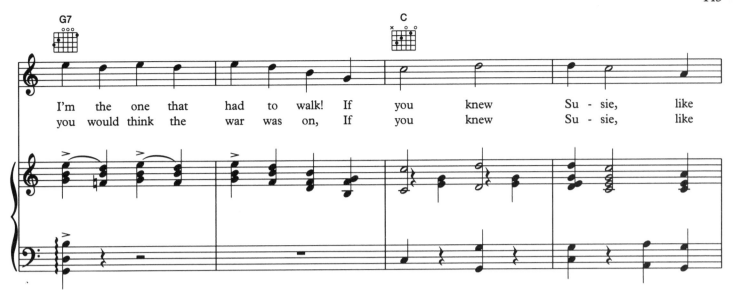

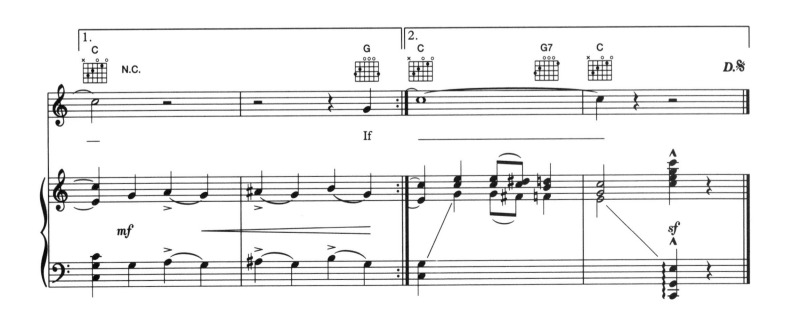

I'M NOBODY'S BABY

Words and Music by BENNY DAVIS, MILTON AGER
and LESTER SANTLY

INDIAN LOVE CALL

Words by OTTO HARBACH and OSCAR HAMMERSTEIN II
Music by RUDOLF FRIML

JUST A GIGOLO

Words and Music by JULIUS BRAMMER, LEONELLO CASUCCI
and IRVING CAESAR

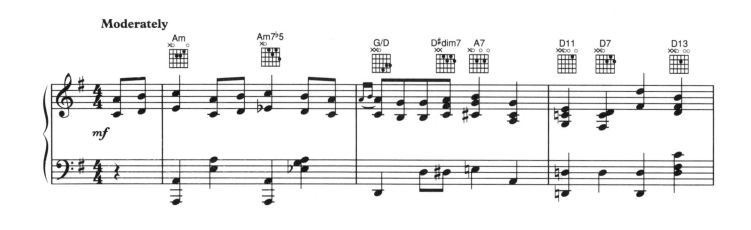

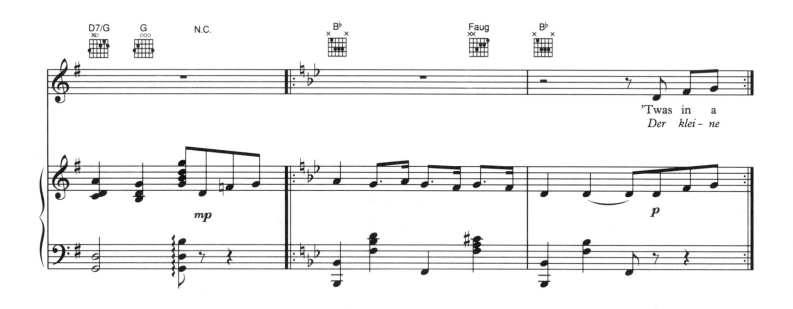

'Twas in a
Der klei - ne

Pa - ris ca - fé that first I found him,__ he was a French - man, a he - ro of the
Leut - nant, er war der be - ste Rei - ter,__ und al - le Her - zen, sie flo - gen ihm gleich

154

there will come a day, youth will pass a-way, then, what will they say a-
U - ni - form pas - sée, lieb - chen sagt: A - dieu! Schö - ne welt, du gingst in

-bout me? When the end comes I know they'll say 'Just a gi - go - lo,' as
Fran - sen! Wenn das Herz dir auch bricht, zeig' ein la - chen - des Ge - sicht, man

life goes on with - out me. - out me.
zahlt und du mußt tan - zen! tan - zen!

K-RA-ZY FOR YOU

Music and Lyrics by GEORGE GERSHWIN and IRA GERSHWIN

THE LAZIEST GAL IN TOWN

Words and Music by COLE PORTER

I've a beau, his name is Jim,— he loves me— and I love him; but he tells— me I'm too prim, that means I'm— too slow. I let him rant,— I let him rave,— I

LET'S MISBEHAVE

Words and Music by COLE PORTER

LET'S DO IT (LET'S FALL IN LOVE)

Words and Music by COLE PORTER
Additional Words by NOËL COWARD

When the lit- tle blue-bird, who has ne - ver said a word, starts to sing; 'Spring, spring' when the

lit- tle blue - bell, in the bot - tom of the dell, starts to ring: 'Ding, ding' when the

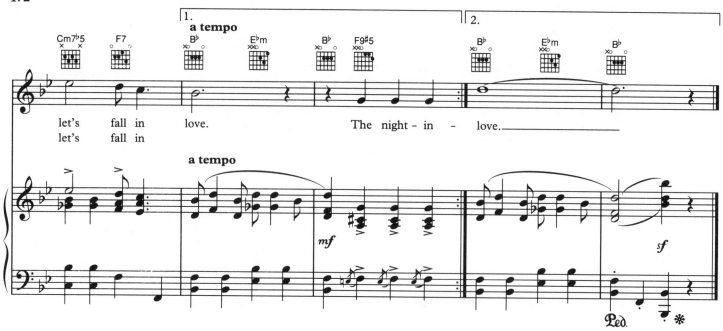

let's   fall in   love.   The night - in - love._____
let's   fall in

Verse 1:

Mr Irving Berlin
Often emphasizes sin
In a charming way
Mr Coward we know
Wrote a song or two to show
Sex was here to stay
Richard Rodgers it's true
Takes a more romantic view
Of that sly biological urge
But it really was Cole
Who contrived to make the whole
Thing merge

Verse 2:

In the Spring of the year
Inhibitions disappear
And our hearts beat high
We had better face the facts
Every gland that overacts
Has an alibi
For each bird and each bee
Each slap-happy sappy tree
Each temptation that lures us along
Is just nature elle-même
Merely singing us the same
Old song

Refrain 1:

He said that Belgians and Dutch do it
Even Hildegarde and Hutch do it
Let's do it, let's fall in love
Monkeys whenever you look do it
Aly Khan and King Farouk do it
Let's do it, let's fall in love
The most recherché cocottes do it
In a luxury flat
Locks, Dunns and Scotts do it
At the drop of a hat
Excited spinsters in spas do it
Duchesses when opening bazaars do it
Let's do it, let's fall in love

Refrain 3:

Girls from the R.A.D.A. do it
B.B.C. announcers may do it
Let's do it, let's fall in love
The Ballet Russe to a man do it
Alfred Lunt and Lynn Fontanne do it
Let's do it, let's fall in love
My kith and kin, more or less, do it
Every uncle and aunt
But I confess to it
I've one cousin who can't
Critics as sour as quince do it
Even Emile Littler and Prince do it
Let's do it, let's fall in love

Refrain 2:

Our leading writers in swarms do it
Somerset and all the Maughams do it
Let's do it, let's fall in love
The Brontës felt that they must do it
Mrs Humphry Ward could just do it
Let's do it, let's fall in love
Anouilh and Sartre - God knows why - do it
As a sort of curse
Eliot and Fry do it
But they do it in verse
Some mystics, as a routine do it
Even Evelyn Waugh and Graham Greene do it
Let's do it, let's fall in love

Refrain 4:

The House of Commons en bloc do it
Civil servants by the clock do it
Let's do it, let's fall in love
Deacons who've done it before do it
Minor canons with a roar do it
Let's do it, let's fall in love
Some rather rorty old rips do it
When they get a bit tight
Government Whips do it
If it takes them all night
Old mountain goats in ravines do it
Probably we'll live to see machines do it
Let's do it, let's fall in love

MISTAKES

Words by EDGAR LESLIE
Music by EVERETT LYNTON

THE MAN I LOVE

Music and Lyrics by
GEORGE GERSHWIN and IRA GERSHWIN

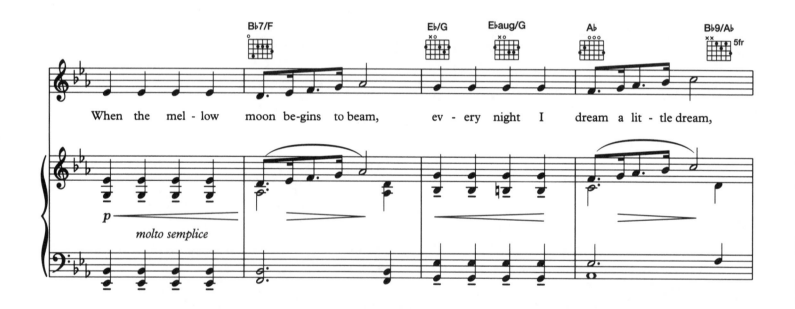

When the mel - low moon be-gins to beam, ev - ery night I dream a lit - tle dream,

and of course Prince Charm-ing is the theme, the he for me. Al -

MOONLIGHT AND ROSES

Words by BEN BLACK and CHARLES DANIELS
Music adapted from Andatino in Db by EDWIN LEMARE

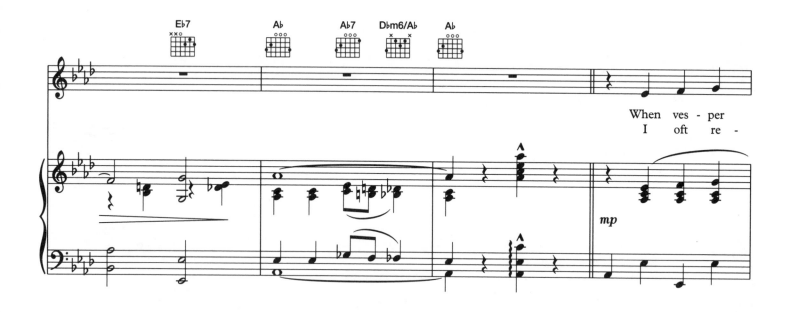

fall._____ 'Tis then my heart grows fon - der as through the
dreams,_____ and then a - las, we part - ed, you left me

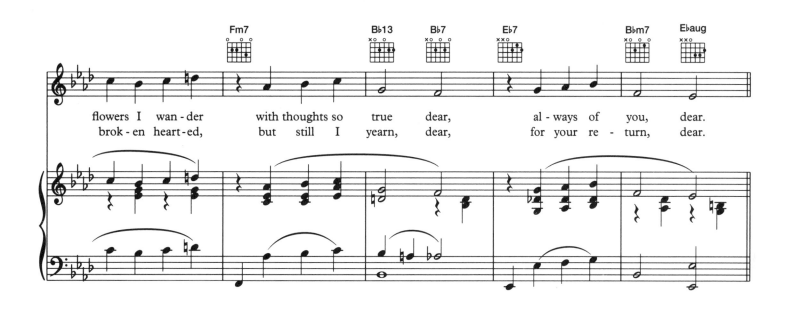

flowers I wan - der with thoughts so true dear, al - ways of you, dear.
brok - en heart - ed, but still I yearn, dear, for your re - turn, dear.

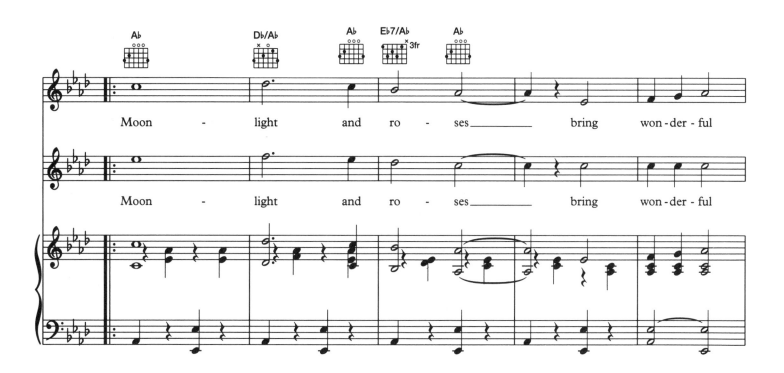

Moon - light and ro - ses_____ bring won - der - ful

Moon - light and ro - ses_____ bring won - der - ful

MORE THAN YOU KNOW

Words by BILLY ROSE and EDWARD ELISCU
Music by VINCENT YOUMANS

186

MOUNTAIN GREENERY

Words by LORENZ HART
Music by RICHARD RODGERS

193

MY YIDDISHE MOMME

Words by JACK YELLEN
Music by JACK YELLEN and LEW POLLACK

MUSKRAT RAMBLE

Words by RAY GILBERT
Music by EDWARD ORY

202

NOBODY KNOWS YOU
WHEN YOU'RE DOWN AND OUT

Words and Music by JIMMIE COX

Slow Blues

Once I lived the life of a mil-lion-aire.__ Spend-ing my mon-ey, I

didn't care. I car-ried my friends out for a good time__ buy-ing boot-leg lik-ker,__ cham-

-pagne and wine.__ When I be-gan to fall__ so slow__ I

NOBODY'S SWEETHEART

Words by GUS KAHN and BILLY MEYERS
Music by ERNEST ERDMAN and ELMER SCHOEBEL

You were ev-ery-bo-dy's
In a sim-ple gown of

sweet — heart not so long a - go,
ging — ham, I can see you still,

209

ON MOTHER KELLY'S DOORSTEP

Words and Music by GEORGE A STEVENS

THE ONE I LOVE BELONGS TO SOMEBODY ELSE

Words by GUS KAHN
Music by ISHAM JONES

Lyrics (lower staff):

I'm un-hap-py, so un-hap-py, for I can see
I keep try-ing, I keep try-ing to stay a - way

the one I love
it can't be done

don't care for
one sin-gle

ONLY A ROSE

Words by BRIAN HOOKER
Music by RUDOLPH FRIML

ROSE OF THE RIO GRANDE

Words by EDGAR LESLIE
Music by HARRY WARREN and ROSS GORMAN

Pals____ fel - lers and gals____ out in a
Gangs____ on their mus - tangs____ wait at the

lone____ star town.____
can - yon side,____

fair_____ is she._____
pair_____ ap - pear._____

He,_____ proud as can be,_____
Cheers_____ ring in their ears,_____

croons_____ one of his love tunes.
birds_____ sing to these love words:

PASADENA

Words by GRANT CLARKE and EDGAR LESLIE
Music by HARRY WARREN

EMI Music Publishing Ltd, London WC2H 0EA and Redwood Music Ltd, London NW1 8BD

THE RUNAWAY TRAIN

Words by ROBERT E MASSEY
Music by CARSON ROBISON

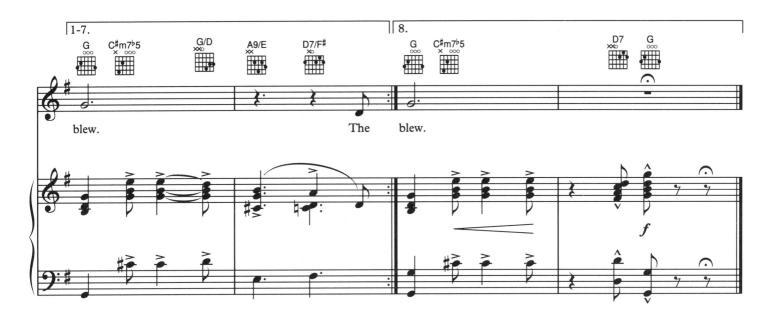

Chorus 2:

The engineer said the train must halt
And she blew - she blew
The engineer said the train must halt
And she blew - she blew
The engineer said the train must halt
He said it was all the fireman's fault
And she blew, blew, blew, blew, blew

Chorus 3:

The fireman said he rang the bell
And she blew - she blew
The fireman said he rang the bell
And she blew - she blew
The fireman said he rang the bell
The engineer said you did like 'FUN'
And she blew, blew, blew, blew, blew

Chorus 4:

The porter got an awful fright
And she blew- she blew
The porter got an awful fright
And she blew - she blew
The porter got an awful fright
He got so scared that he turned white
And she blew, blew, blew, blew, blew

Chorus 5:

A mule was standing in the way
And she blew - she blew
A mule was standing in the way
And she blew - she blew
A mule was standing in the way
And all they found was just his bray
And she blew, blew, blew, blew, blew

Chorus 6:

A drummer sat in the parlour car
And she blew - she blew
A drummer sat in the parlour car
And she blew - she blew
A drummer sat in the parlour car
And he nearly swallowed a fat cigar
And she blew, blew, blew, blew, blew

Chorus 7:

The conductor said there'd be a wreck
And she blew - she blew
The conductor said there'd be a wreck
And she blew - she blew
The conductor said there'd be a wreck
And he felt the chills run up his neck
And she blew, blew, blew, blew, blew

Chorus 8:

The runaway train went over the hill
And she blew - she blew
The runaway train went over the hill
And she blew - she blew
The runaway train went over the hill
And the last we heard she was going still
And she blew, blew, blew, blew, blew

S'POSIN'

Words by ANDY RAZAF
Music by PAUL DENNIKER

A SHIP WITHOUT A SAIL

Words by LORENZ HART
Music by RICHARD RODGERS

He: I don't know what day it is, or if it's dark or fair; Some-

She: When love leaves you all a-lone, you're liv-ing in the past;

-how, that's just the way it is, and I don't real-ly

Then you feel so small a-lone, and oh! The world seems

SAY IT WITH MUSIC

Words and Music by IRVING BERLIN

Girl: Mu - sic is a lang - uage lov - ers un - der - stand,
Boy: There's a ten - der mes - sage deep down in my heart,

Me - lo - dy and ro - mance wan - der hand in hand.
Some - thing you should know, but how am I to start?

SHAKING THE BLUES AWAY

Words and Music by IRVING BERLIN

There's an old su-per-sti-tion 'way down south.

Ev-'ry bo-dy be-lieves that trou-ble won't stay

S-H-I-N-E

Words by CECIL MACK and LEW BROWN
Music by FORD T DABNEY

SOMETIMES I'M HAPPY

Words by IRVING CAESAR and CLIFFORD GREY
Music by VINCENT YOUMANS

1. *He:* Ev - ery day — seems
2. *He:* Stars are smil - ing at me

like a year, —
from your eyes. —

sweet - heart, when — you
She: Sun - beams now — there will be

Warner/Chappell Music Ltd, London W1Y 3FA

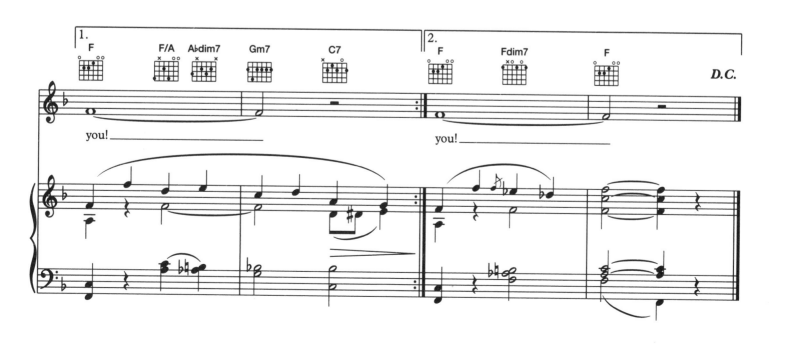

(I'LL BUILD A) STAIRWAY TO PARADISE

Music and Lyrics by GEORGE GERSHWIN, BUDDY DE SYLVA
and ARTHUR FRANCIS

STRIKE UP THE BAND

Music and Lyrics by
GEORGE GERSWHIN and IRA GERSHWIN

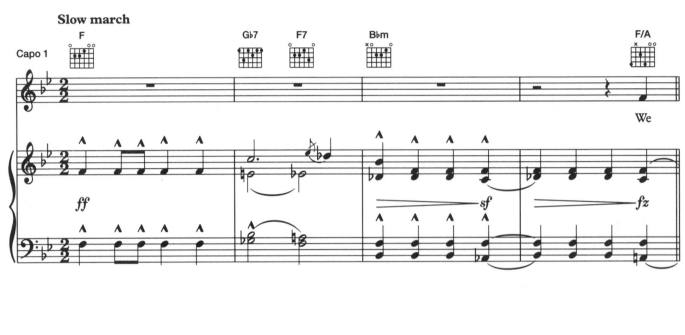

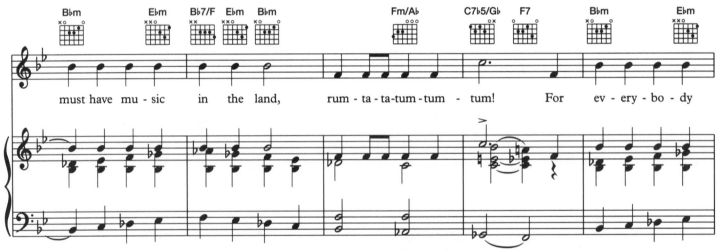

'TAIN'T NOBODY'S BIZ-NESS IF I DO

Words and Music by PORTER GRAINGER and EVERETT ROBBINS

There ain't no-thin' I can do nor no-thin' I can
Af-ter all, the way to do is, 'do just as you

say_____ that folks don't cri-ti-cise me,
please'_____ re-gard-less of their talk-in'

THAT OLD FASHIONED MOTHER OF MINE

Words by WORTON DAVID
Music by HORATIO NICHOLLS

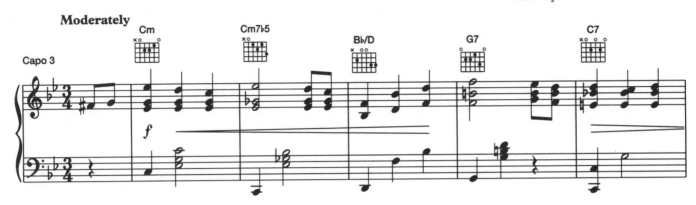

There are col - leens with eyes just as
There are jew - els I know that set

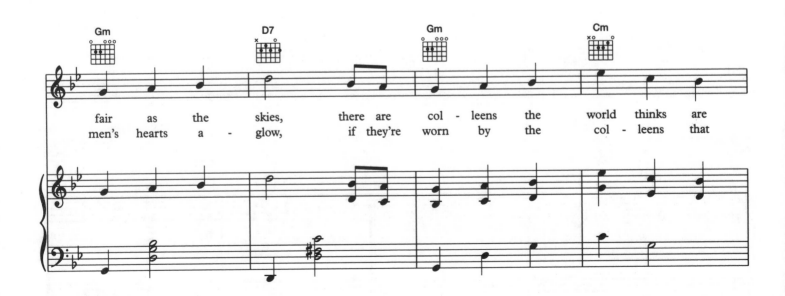

fair as the skies, there are col - leens the world thinks are
men's hearts a - glow, if they're worn by the col - leens that

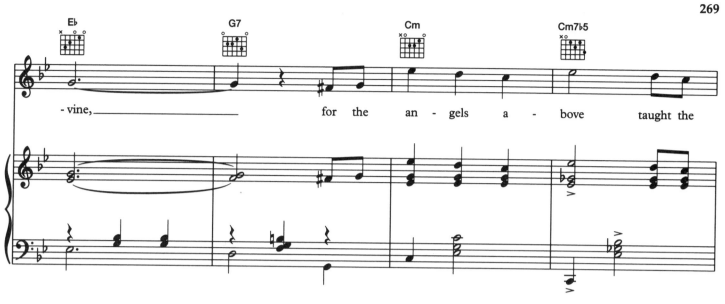

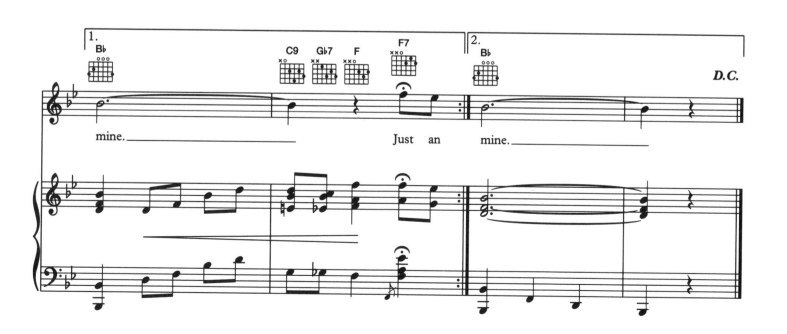

THERE'S A BLUE RIDGE ROUND MY HEART VIRGINIA

Words by ALFRED BRYAN
Music by FRED PHILLIPS and IRA SCHUSTER

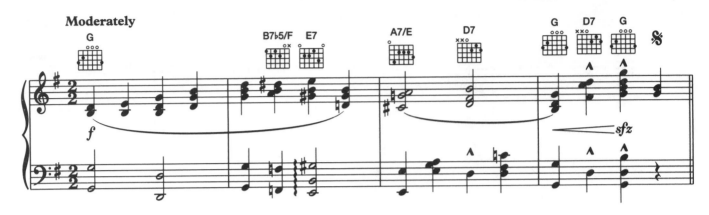

Vir - gin - ia State, it seems of late
Birds in the tree,_ hum of the bee,_

you're al - ways in my dreams, I miss your pale moon - beams,
tell them I'll soon be home. Each lit - tle rose that grows,

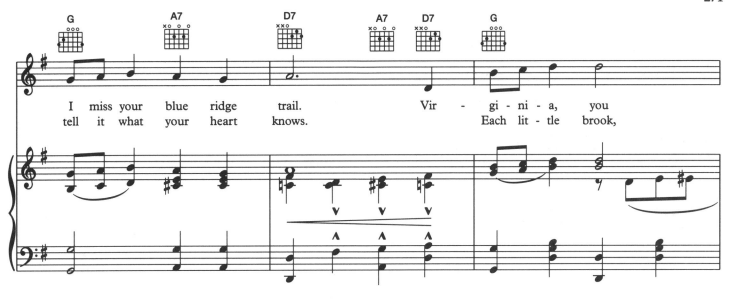

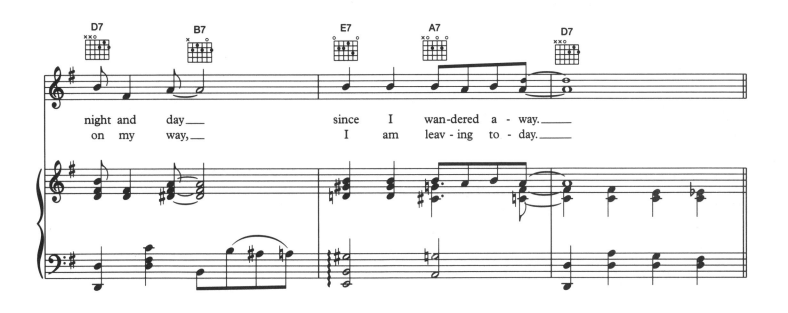

THOU SWELL

Words by LORENZ HART
Music by RICHARD RODGERS

He: Babe, we are well met, as in a spell met, I lift my hel - met, San - dy,___ you're
She: Thy words are queer, Sir, un - to mine ear, Sir, yet thou'rt a dear, Sir, to me.___ Thou

___ just dan - dy, for_____ just this here lad.
___ couldst woo_____ me, now_____ could'st thou try, knight.

THEY'RE CHANGING GUARD AT BUCKINGHAM PALACE

Words by A.A. MILNE
Music by HAROLD FRASER-SIMSON

In March time (very martial)

TOOT TOOT TOOTSIE, GOO'BYE

Words and Music by GUS KAHN, ERNIE ERDMAN,
DAN RUSSO and TED FIORITO

WHAT IS THIS THING CALLED LOVE?

Words and Music by COLE PORTER

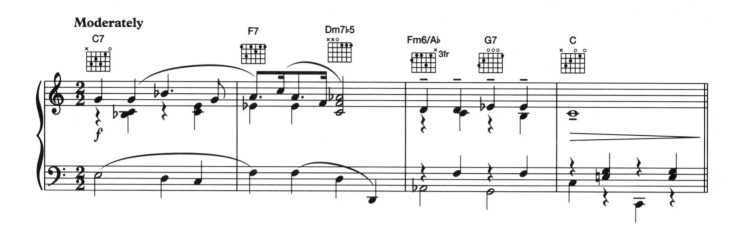

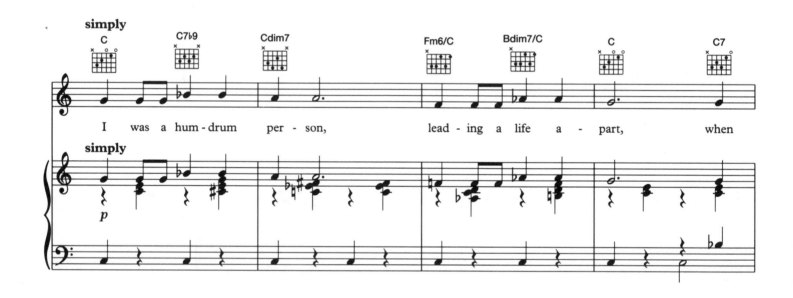

I was a hum-drum per-son, lead-ing a life a-part, when

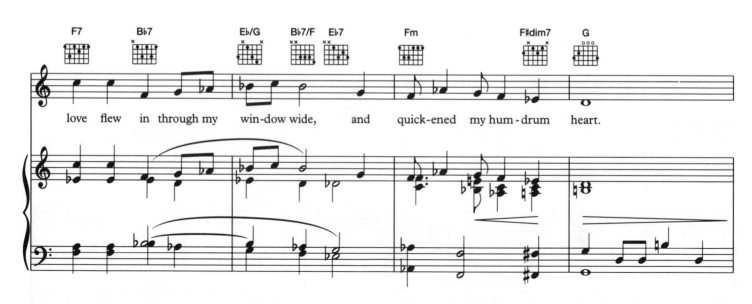

love flew in through my win-dow wide, and quick-ened my hum-drum heart.

-way. That's why I ask the Lord_____ in hea-ven a-

-bove, what is this thing_____ called

love? What love?_____

WHEN MY BABY SMILES AT ME

Words by TED LEWIS and ANDREW B STERLING
Music by BILL MUNRO

WITHOUT A SONG

Words by BILLY ROSE and EDWARD ELISCU
Music by VINCENT YOUMANS

Without a song the day would never end; without a song the road would never bend; when things go wrong a man ain't

WHAT'LL I DO?

Words and Music by IRVING BERLIN

Gone is the ro-mance that was so di-vine.____ 'Tis bro-ken and
Do you re-mem-ber a night filled with bliss?____ The moon-light was

can-not be mend — ed. You must go your way and
soft-ly de-scend — ing. Your lips and my lips and were

I must go mine.____ But now that our love dreams have
tied with a kiss.____ A kiss with an un-hap — py

WHEN YOU'RE SMILING

Words and Music by MARK FISHER,
JOE GOODWIN and LARRY SHAY

WHO'S SORRY NOW?

Words by BERT KALMAR and HARRY RUBY
Music by TED SNYDER

WAY DOWN YONDER IN NEW ORLEANS

Words and Music by
HENRY CREAMER and TURNER LAYTON

Guess! Where do you think I'm go - ing when the nights start grow-ing long?_____ I
Guess! What do you think I'm think - ing when I'm think - ing all night long?_____ I

ain't go - ing east, I ain't go - ing west, I ain't go - ing o - ver the cuc-koo's nest, I'm
ain't think-ing this, I ain't think-ing that, I can - not be think-ing a - bout your hat,__ my

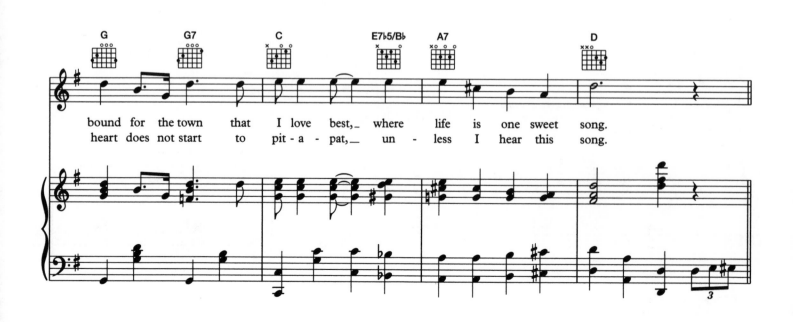

bound for the town that I love best,_ where life is one sweet song.
heart does not start to pit - a - pat,__ un - less I hear this song.

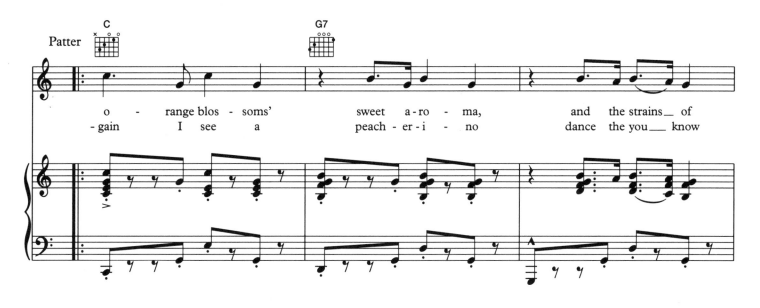

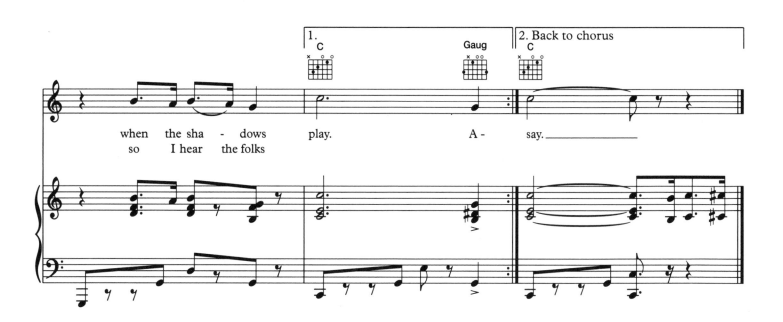

YOU DO SOMETHING TO ME

Words and Music by COLE PORTER

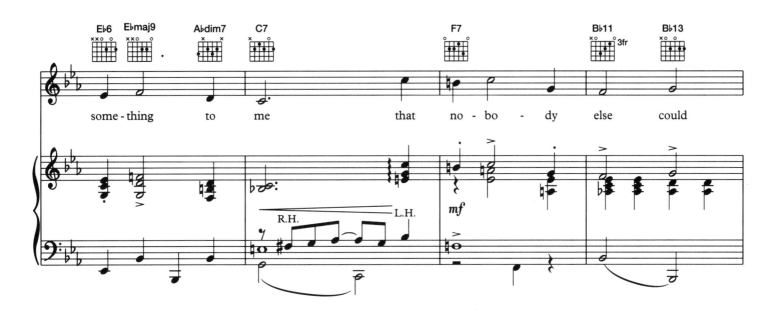

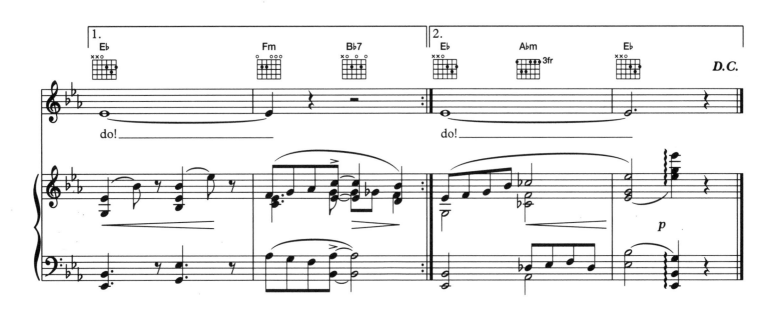

YES! WE HAVE NO BANANAS

Words and Music by FRANK SILVER and IRVING CONN

YOU'RE IN KENTUCKY SURE AS YOU'RE BORN

Words and Music by GEORGE A LITTLE,
HAVEN GILLESPIE and LARRY SHAY

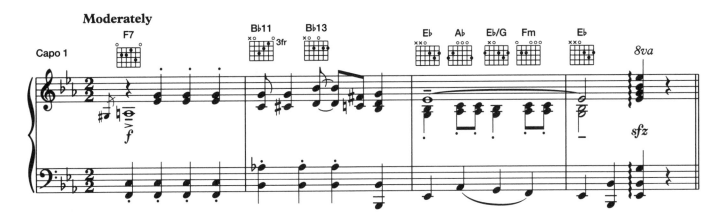

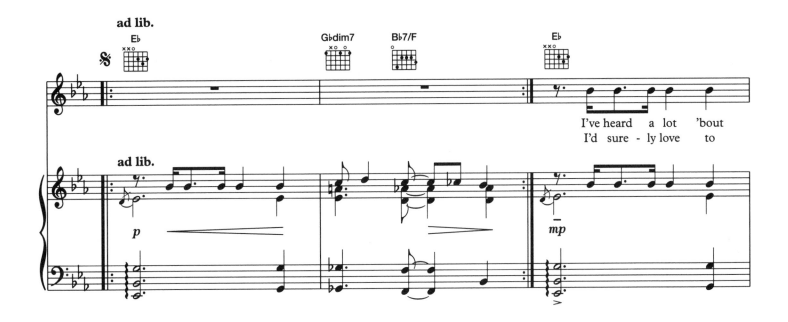

I've heard a lot 'bout
I'd sure - ly love to

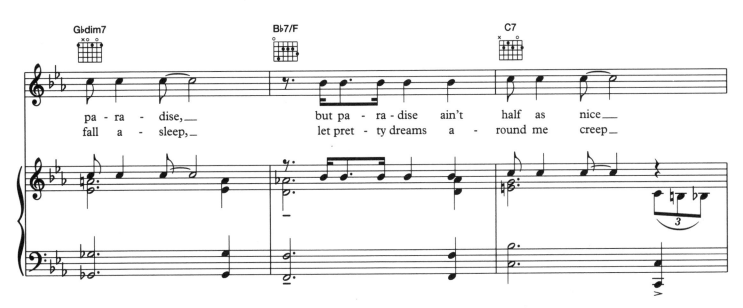

pa - ra - dise,___ but pa - ra - dise ain't half as nice___
fall a - sleep,___ let pret - ty dreams a - round me creep___

100 YEARS OF POPULAR MUSIC

International
MUSIC
Publications

IMP's Exciting New Series!

100 YEARS OF POPULAR MUSIC

Vol. 1 - 9817A

Vol. 1 - 9819A

9816A

Vol. 1 - 9821A

Vol. 1 - 9823A

Vol. 2 - 9818A

Vol. 2 - 9820A

Vol. 2 - 9822A

Vol. 2 - 9824A

IMP
International
MUSIC
Publications

IMP's Exciting New Series!

100 YEARS OF POPULAR MUSIC

Vol. 1 - 9825A

Vol. 1 - 9827A

Vol. 1 - 9829A

Vol. 1 - 9831A

Vol. 2 - 9826A

Vol. 2 - 9828A

Vol. 2 - 9830A

Vol. 2 - 9832A

Vol. 2 - 9833A

International
MUSIC
Publications

IMP's Exciting New Series!